ULTIMA
CHART HITS

C000194957

WISE PUBLICATIONS
PART OF THE MUSIC SALES GROUP
LONDON / NEW YORK / PARIS / SYDNEY / COPENHAGEN / BERLIN / MADRID / HONG KONG / TOKYO

ALSO AVAILABLE IN THE REALLY EASY PIANO SERIES...

ABBA
25 GREAT HITS. ORDER NO. AM980430

CHILDREN'S FAVOURITES
20 POPULAR HITS. ORDER NO. AM998745

CHRISTMAS
24 FESTIVE CHART HITS. ORDER NO. AM980496

CLASSICAL FAVOURITES
24 WELL-KNOWN FAVOURITES. ORDER NO. AM993366

COLDPLAY
20 SONGS FROM COLDPLAY. ORDER NO. AM989593

ELTON JOHN
24 CLASSIC SONGS. ORDER NO. AM987844

FRANK SINATRA
21 CLASSIC SONGS. ORDER NO. AM987833

GREAT FILM SONGS
22 BIG FILM HITS. ORDER NO. AM993344

GREAT SHOWSTOPPERS
20 POPULAR STAGE SONGS. ORDER NO. AM993355

JAZZ GREATS
22 JAZZ FAVOURITES. ORDER NO. AM1000857

LOVE SONGS
22 CLASSIC LOVE SONGS. ORDER NO. AM989582

MICHAEL JACKSON
19 CLASSIC HITS. ORDER NO. AM1000604

MORE 21ST CENTURY HITS
21 POPULAR HITS. ORDER NO. AM996534

MOZART
22 CLASSICAL FAVOURITES. ORDER NO. AM1000648

NEW CHART HITS
19 BIG CHART HITS. ORDER NO. AM996523

NO. 1 HITS
22 POPULAR CLASSICS. ORDER NO. AM993388

POP HITS
22 GREAT SONGS. ORDER NO. AM980408

SHOWSTOPPERS
24 STAGE HITS. ORDER NO. AM982784

TV HITS
25 POPULAR HITS. ORDER NO. AM985435

60S HITS
25 CLASSIC HITS. ORDER NO. AM985402

70S HITS
25 CLASSIC SONGS. ORDER NO. AM985413

80S HITS
25 POPULAR HITS. ORDER NO. AM985424

90S HITS
24 POPULAR HITS. ORDER NO. AM987811

50 FABULOUS SONGS
FROM POP SONGS TO CLASSICAL THEMES. ORDER NO. AM999449

50 GREAT SONGS
FROM POP SONGS TO CLASSICAL THEMES. ORDER NO. AM995643

50 HIT SONGS
FROM POP HITS TO JAZZ CLASSICS. ORDER NO. AM1000615

PIANO TUTOR
FROM FIRST STEPS TO PLAYING IN A WIDE
RANGE OF STYLES — FAST!. ORDER NO. AM996303

ALL TITLES CONTAIN BACKGROUND NOTES FOR EACH SONG PLUS
PLAYING TIPS AND HINTS.

PUBLISHED BY
WISE PUBLICATIONS
14-15 BERNERS STREET, LONDON, W1T 3LJ, UK.

EXCLUSIVE DISTRIBUTORS:
MUSIC SALES LIMITED
DISTRIBUTION CENTRE, NEWMARKET ROAD, BURY ST EDMUNDS,
SUFFOLK, IP33 3YB, UK.
MUSIC SALES PTY LIMITED
UNITS 3-4, 17 WILLFOX STREET, CONDELL PARK
NSW 2200, AUSTRALIA.

ORDER NO. AM1010515
ISBN 978-1-78305-945-4
THIS BOOK © COPYRIGHT 2015 BY WISE PUBLICATIONS,
A DIVISION OF MUSIC SALES LIMITED.

ARRANGED BY BARRIE CARSON TURNER.
EDITED BY JENNI NOREY.
PRINTED IN THE EU.

YOUR GUARANTEE OF QUALITY
AS PUBLISHERS, WE STRIVE TO PRODUCE EVERY BOOK TO THE HIGHEST
COMMERCIAL STANDARDS. THE MUSIC HAS BEEN FRESHLY ENGRAVED AND
THE BOOK HAS BEEN CAREFULLY DESIGNED TO MINIMISE AWKWARD PAGE
TURNS AND TO MAKE PLAYING FROM IT A REAL PLEASURE.
PARTICULAR CARE HAS BEEN GIVEN TO SPECIFYING ACID-FREE, NEUTRAL-
SIZED PAPER MADE FROM PULPS WHICH HAVE NOT BEEN ELEMENTAL
CHLORINE BLEACHED. THIS PULP IS FROM FARMED SUSTAINABLE FORESTS
AND WAS PRODUCED WITH SPECIAL REGARD FOR THE ENVIRONMENT.
THROUGHOUT, THE PRINTING AND BINDING HAVE BEEN PLANNED TO
ENSURE A STURDY, ATTRACTIVE PUBLICATION WHICH SHOULD GIVE YEARS
OF ENJOYMENT. IF YOUR COPY FAILS TO MEET OUR HIGH STANDARDS,
PLEASE INFORM US AND WE WILL GLADLY REPLACE IT.

WWW.MUSICSALES.COM

ULTIMATE CHART HITS

All About That Bass

Words & Music by Kevin Kadish & Meghan Trainor

After being offered to other artists, including Beyoncé, it was finally decided that cowriter Meghan Trainor should be the one to add her vocals to the track. This pop-fuelled tune with a doo-wop vibe was her debut single, and reached No. 1 in over 10 countries.

Hints & Tips: The bass line to this song, played by the left hand, is repetitive throughout. Get this pattern under your fingers before trying to fit the right hand to it.

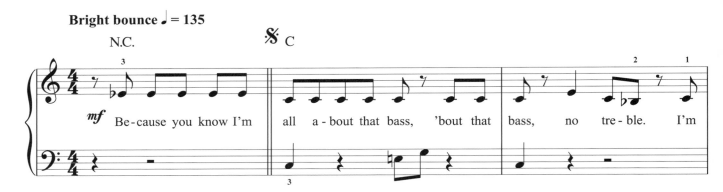

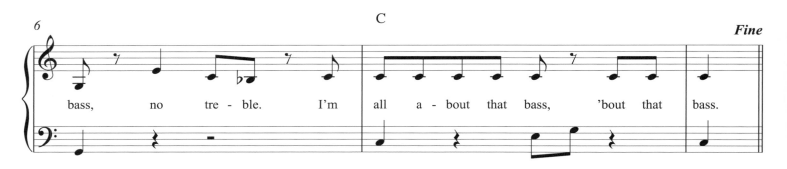

All Of Me

Words and Music by John Stephens and Toby Gad

This simple but effective piano and vocal based song hit the No. 1 spot in several countries, including the US, Australia, Ireland and Canada. It was written for John Legend's then-fiancé Chrissy Teigen, who he married in 2013. The video shows clips from the couple's honeymoon.

Hints & Tips: Set a metronome going and listen to the tempo first, so you know how fast the crotchets need to be. The melody is expressive and should be played smooth and flowing.

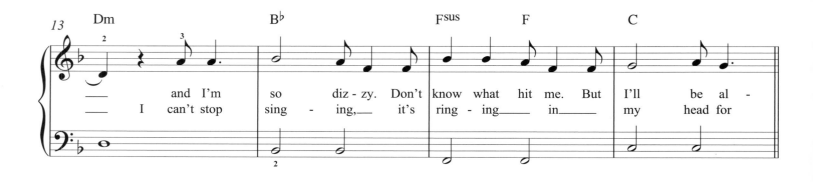

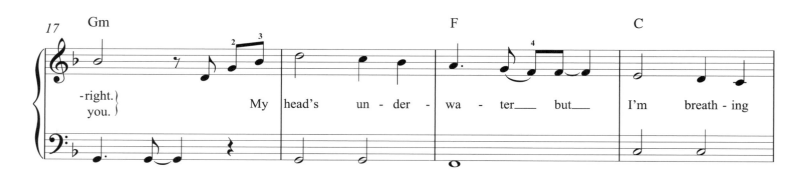

Blame It On Me

Words & Music by Joel Pott & George Ezra Barnett

'Blame It On Me' was released as the fourth single from George Ezra's debut album, *Wanted On Voyage*. The music video shows the singer enduring one bad event after another, culminating in getting caught in the crossfire between the police and a gang of masked figures. Thankfully, he walks away unscathed.

Hints & Tips: There's a big stretch in the right hand at the start, from middle C to the A above. Make sure you can play this and any subsequent leaps smoothly, to avoid the melody sounding jarred.

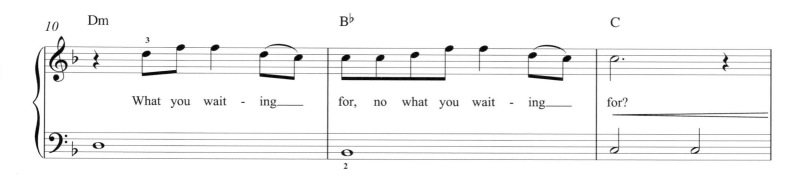

What you wait - ing_____ for, no what you wait - ing_____ for?

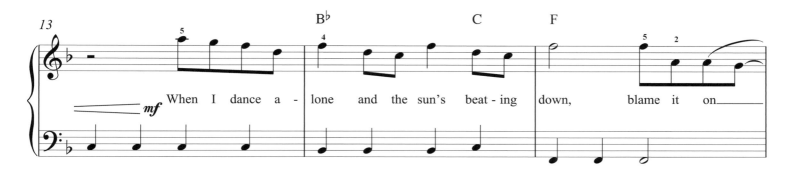

When I dance a - lone and the sun's beat - ing down, blame it on_____

_____ me._____ When I lose con - trol and the veil's_ o - ver - used,_

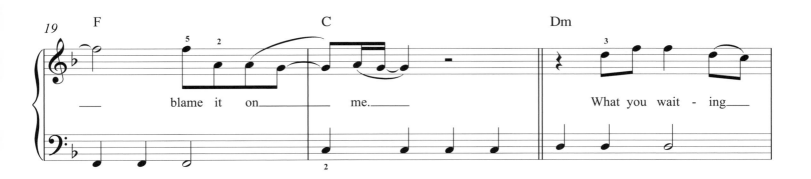

blame it on_____ me._____ What you wait - ing_____

for, no what you wait - ing_____ for? *mp* 3. Caught

in the tide___ of blos - som, caught in the car - ni - val. Your

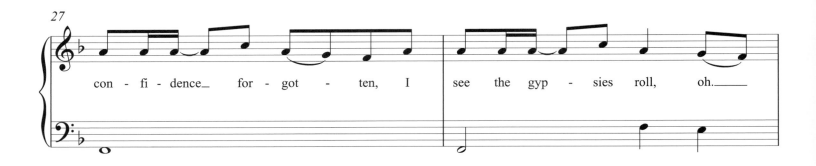

con - fi - dence___ for - got - ten, I see the gyp - sies roll, oh.___

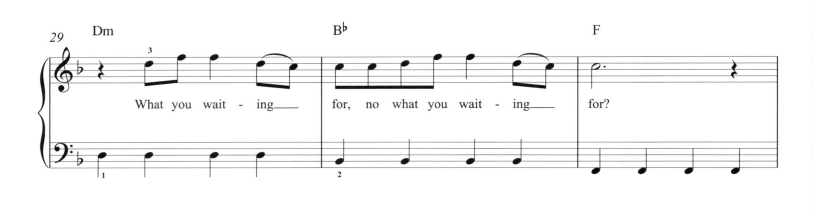

What you wait - ing___ for, no what you wait - ing___ for?

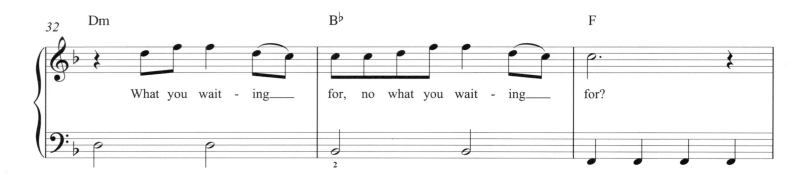

What you wait - ing___ for, no what you wait - ing___ for?

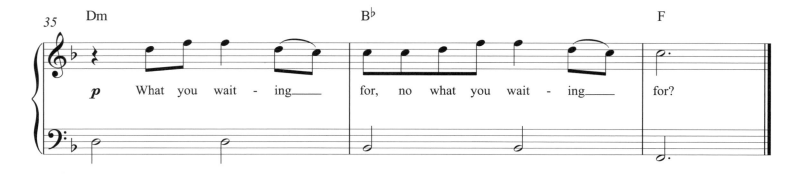

What you wait - ing___ for, no what you wait - ing___ for?

Ghost

Words & Music by Ryan Tedder, Noel Zancanella
& Ella Henderson

Ella Henderson was a finalist in the ninth series of *The X Factor*. Despite not winning the competition, 'Ghost', her first single, went straight to the top of the UK singles chart. Her debut album *Chapter One* also peaked at No. 1 in its first week.

Hints & Tips: You'll notice that the repeated section on the last page (bar 25) has two dynamics marked. This means that the passage should be played *mp* first time and *mf* second time.

his name.___ And that's when my love was___ burn - ing. Yeah, it's still burn - ing.___

I keep go - ing to the riv - er to pray___

___ 'cause I need some - thing that can wash out the pain.___

___ And at most I'm sleep - ing all these de - mons a - way.___

___ But your ghost, the ghost of you, it keeps me a - wake.

ghost of you, it keeps me a - wake.

Don't Stop

Words & Music by Stephen Robson, Marie Maud Stewart,
Michael Busbee, Luke Hemmings & Calum Hood

Written as something of an anti-bullying campaign after one of the band members announced on Twitter that his sister was being picked on at school, the video for 'Don't Stop' sees the Australian four-piece dressed as super heroes trying to do good deeds.

Hints & Tips: This is a fun song so try to keep it light; don't let the repeated left hand crotchets in the chorus sound too heavy.

Jealous

**Words & Music by Timothy McKenzie, Josh Kear
& Natalie Hemby**

Singer-songwriter Labrinth penned the lyrics to this song, which is about his father walking out when he was young. He explained in an interview that "It's kind of written from the perspective of how my family felt at the time, but I wanted to write it so anyone could dig into the song and relate it to their own situation."

Hints & Tips: Even though this soft song should be played delicately, try to make sure the melody comes out clearly over the top of the left hand accompaniment.

Only Love Can Hurt Like This

Words & Music by Diane Warren

Recorded by English artist Paloma Faith, this was written by American songwriter Diane Warren, who has composed hits for many prominent artists in the past, including Aerosmith's 'I Don't Want To Miss A Thing' and Cher's 'If I Could Turn Back Time'.

Hints & Tips: You'll need to count both the notes and the rests carefully, as the beat should be kept strong and steady. To make sure it's as accurate as possible, try playing along with a metronome.

Real Love

Words & Music by John Lennon

Tom Odell's cover of this John Lennon song was used in the 2014 John Lewis Christmas advert campaign. Several rough versions were recorded by Lennon between 1979 and 1980, but the song was eventually revisited in full in 1995 when the surviving Beatles members revived the track for the *Beatles Anthology*.

Hints & Tips: Have a look through the whole song before you begin and note where all the accidentals are. The ending is quite repetitive, so make the most of the dynamics to give it some shape.

23

Rather Be

Words & Music by James Napier, Grace Chatto
& Jack Patterson

This UK No. 1 spent four weeks at the top of the charts, was the third fastest-selling single of 2014, and for a portion of that year held the record for most streams in a single week on Spotify. The catchy instrumental hook has been used in Marks & Spencer food adverts.

Hints & Tips: From bar 34, the rhythms get a little trickier. Try clapping the right hand rhythm, and then the left hand rhythm, and then put them together once you've got the hang of them both.

Shake It Off

Words & Music by Max Martin, Taylor Swift
& Shellback

The lead single from her fifth studio album, *1989*, went straight to the No. 1 spot on the US Billboard Hot 100. The lyrics are about Swift learning to not care what the critics or the press say about her, stating "You can either let it get to you … [or] you just shake it off."

Hints & Tips: During the chorus (from bar 25) the fingering is fairly awkward, with the third finger crossing over the thumb in places. Practise these bits separately until you can play them smoothly.

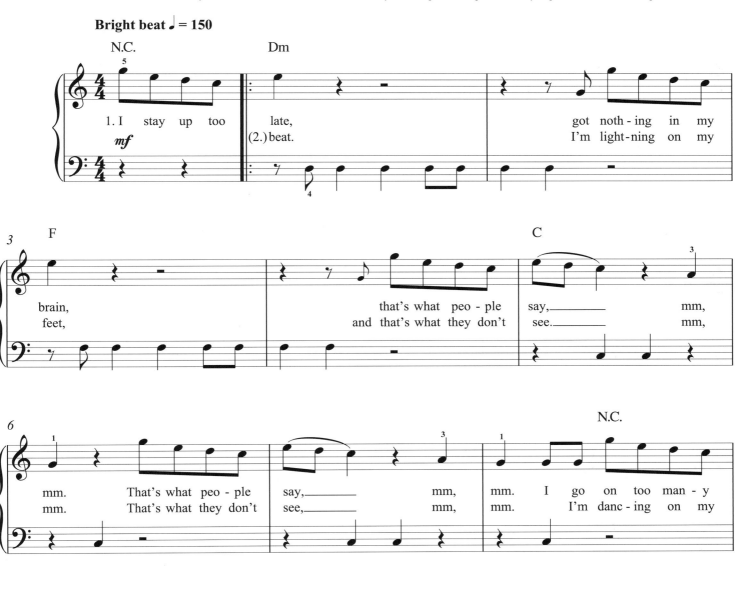

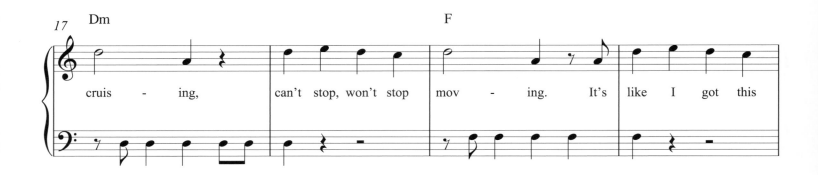

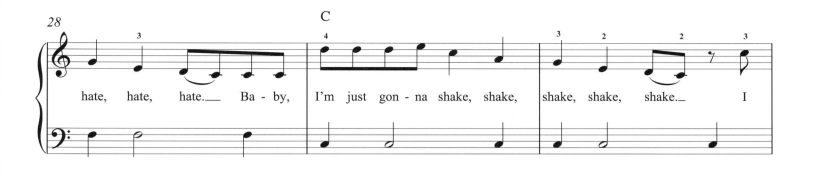

hate, hate, hate.__ Ba - by, I'm just gon - na shake, shake, shake, shake, shake.__ I

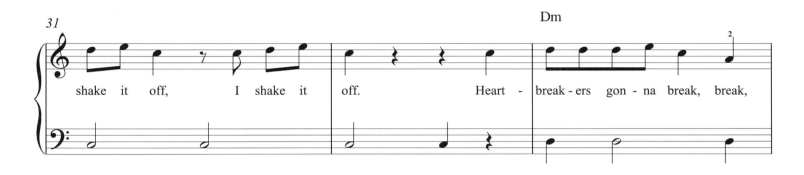

shake it off, I shake it off. Heart - break - ers gon - na break, break,

break, break, break, and the fak - ers gon - na fake, fake, fake, fake, fake.__ Ba - by,

I'm just gon - na shake, shake, shake, shake, shake.__ I shake it off, I shake it

off. 2. I nev - er miss a off.

Rude

**Words & Music by Nasri Atweh, Adam Messinger,
Ben Spivak, Mark Pellizzer & Alexander Tanasijczuk**

This song by Magic! was the first single from a Canadian band to top the US Billboard Hot 100 since Nickleback achieved this success in 2001 with their hit 'How You Remind Me'. Despite this accomplishment 'Rude' only reached No. 6 on the equivalent Canadian chart.

Hints & Tips: The off-beat rhythm in the left hand is what creates the reggae feel to this song. Play these sections through on their own a few times until you've got the hang of how it goes.

Superheroes

Words & Music by Mark Sheehan, Daniel O'Donoghue
& James Barry

A song that celebrates everyday heroes, 'Superheroes' was the lead single from The Script's 2014 album *No Sound Without Silence*. Despite its popularity amongst critics, the song failed to reach No. 1 in the UK Singles Charts, peaking at No. 3.

Hints & Tips: There are lots of semiquavers to deal with in the right hand, so practise this at a slower tempo first and then build up the speed.

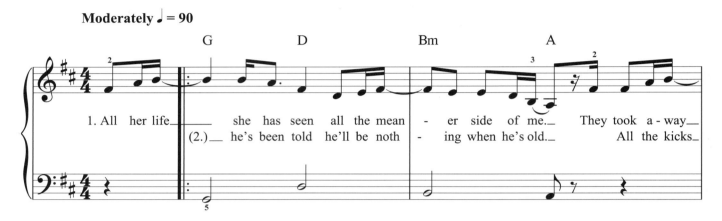

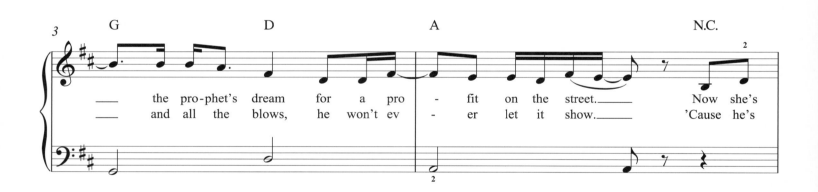

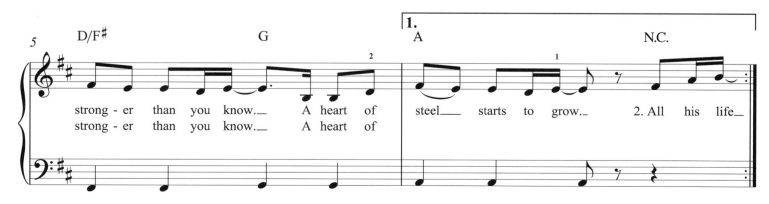

Stay With Me

**Words & Music by Tom Petty, Jeff Lynne,
James Napier, Sam Smith & William Phillips**

The video for 'Stay With Me' shows singer Sam Smith being backed by the London-based Enchorus gospel choir,
though they didn't sing on the track itself; the gospel-choir effect was created by layering the singer's vocals.

Hints & Tips: It may look as if there are some fast rhythms here, but as the piece is set at a fairly slow tempo
they shouldn't prove too much of a challenge; just take it steady.

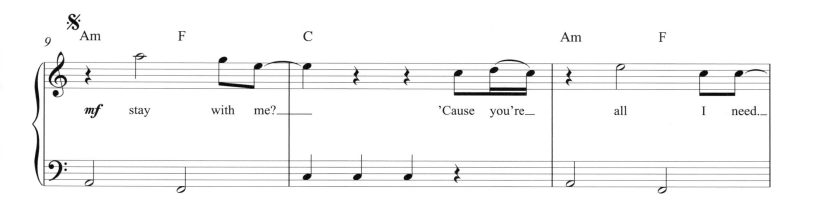

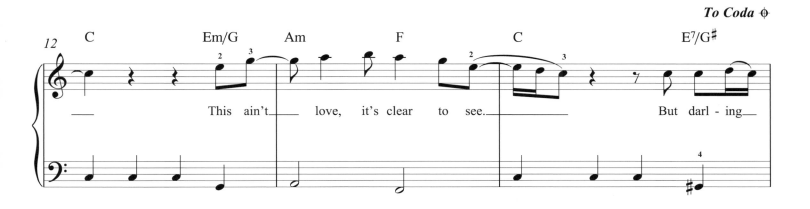

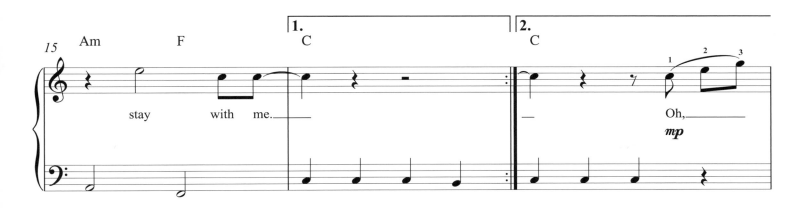

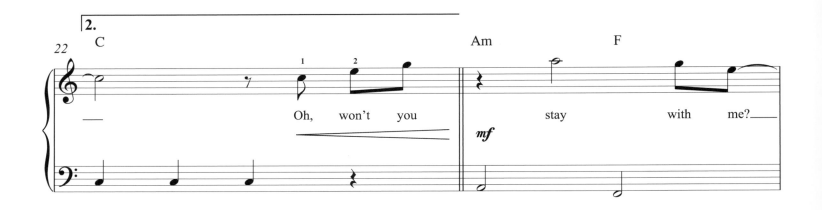

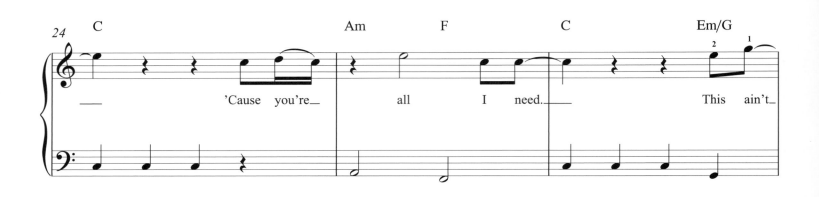

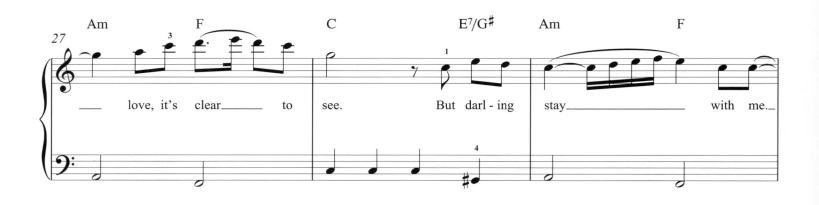

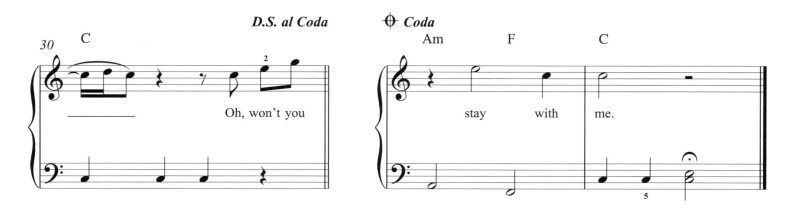

Steal My Girl

**Words & Music by Wayne Hector, John Ryan,
Julian Bunetta, Ed Drewett, Liam Payne & Louis Tomlinson**

The video for this song features actor Danny DeVito as the madcap director. Set in the middle of a desert, it incorporates sumo wrestlers, acrobats, ballet dancers and several circus animals; not to mention the One Direction boys themselves!

Hints & Tips: Use the steady, on-the-beat minims in the left hand to help place those trickier right hand rhythms at the start.

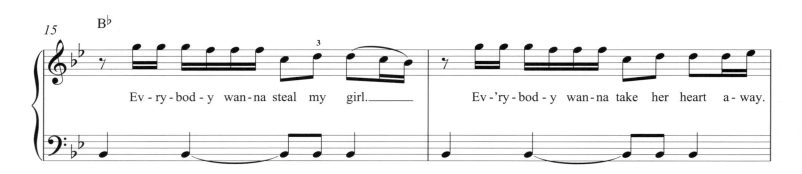

These Days

**Words & Music by Mark Owen, Gary Barlow,
Howard Donald, Jamie Norton & Benjamin Weaver**

'These Days' is the first single to be released by Take That since they became a trio. It became their twelfth No. 1 single, and the first in 6 years. All three sing lead vocals on this upbeat pop number that harks back to the earlier days of the group.

Hints & Tips: Take note of the structure. Mark in pencil where the sign is to repeat back to and also the final bar (*Fine*), so you're not caught out.

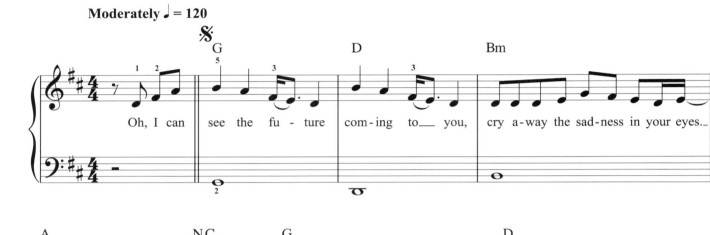

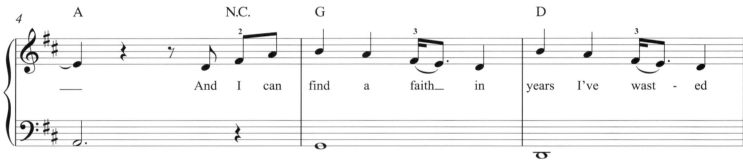

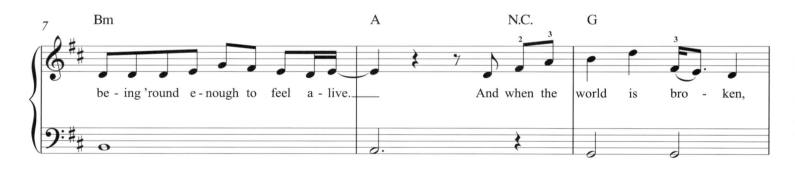

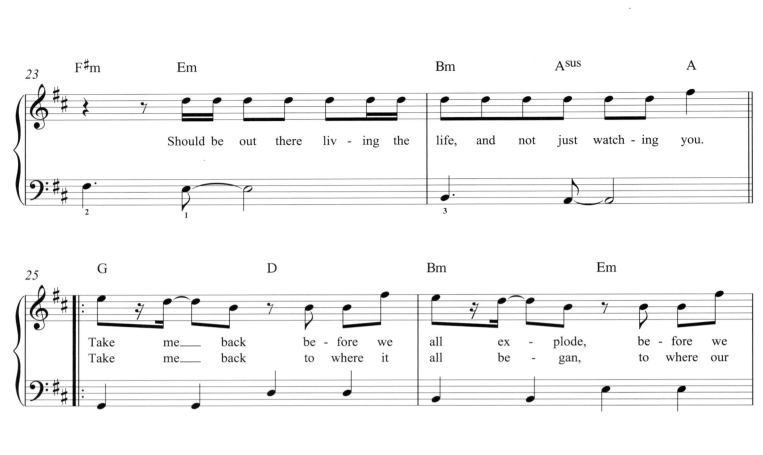

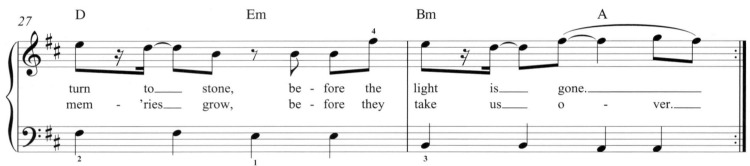

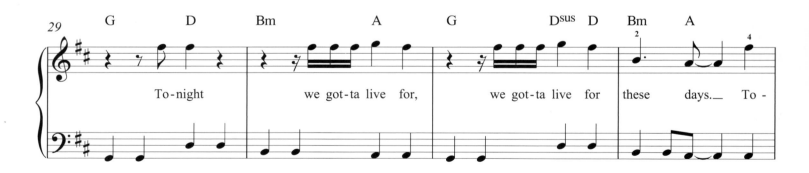

D.S. al Fine

Thinking Out Loud

Words & Music by Ed Sheeran & Amy Wadge

Sheeran famously wrote 'Thinking Out Loud' using a guitar gifted to him by Harry Styles of One Direction, yet piano features heavily on this steady-paced ballad that celebrates the enduring quality of love and romance. It was one of the last songs to be written on the album *x*.

Hints & Tips: Make the most of the melody, using dynamics to build up to the chorus in bar 25, which should be loud but expressive.

Uptown Funk!

**Words & Music by Mark Ronson, Philip Lawrence, Jeffrey Bhasker,
Peter Hernandez, Nicholaus Williams & Devon Gallaspy**

'Uptown Funk!' was in the charts at the same time as Vance Joy's 'Riptide'. Both songs mention actress Michelle Pfeiffer, though for different reasons: 'Uptown Funk!' makes reference to her role in the movie *Scarface*, while Vance Joy was simply a fan of hers when he was younger.

Hints & Tips: The melody of this song is quite repetitive. Make it more interesting by trying to play it percussively, for example experimenting with articulation, adding staccato etc.

Moderately, heavy beat

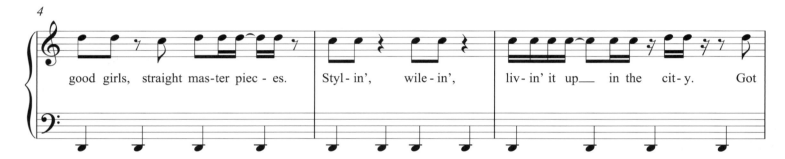